This
High School Musical
Annual belongs to

....

EGMONT
We bring stories to life

HIGH SCHOOL MUSICAL

ANNUAL 2009

First published in Great Britain 2008 by Egmont UK Limited,
239 Kensington High Street, London W8 6SA.
© Disney Enterprises, Inc.
Based on the Disney Channel Original Movie
"High School Musical," Written by Peter Barsocchini
Based on "High School Musical 2," Written by Peter Barsocchini
Based on Characters Created by Peter Barsocchini

Editor: Rennie Brown
Designer: Laura Bird

ISBN 978 1 4052 3904 2
5 7 9 10 8 6 4

Printed in Italy
All Rights Reserved

Note to parents: adult supervision is recommended when sharp-pointed items such as scissors are in use.

Inside

High school ID

Check out the **East High** notice board, then flip over and fill in the student ID cards!

School clubs

Varsity Basketball Team
Troy Bolton
Chad Danforth
Zeke Baylor

Scholastic Decathlon Team
Taylor McKessie
Gabriella Montez

Winter Musical Cast
Kelsi Nielsen
Troy Bolton
Gabriella Montez
Sharpay Evans
Ryan Evans

WILDCATS · WILDCATS · WILDCATS · WILDCATS

EAST HIGH RULES!

SHOOT!
SCORE!
WIN!

Team practice after school today! Meet in the gymnasium at 4pm.

GO WILDCATS GO

Would everybody on the school clubs list please report to me after school.

Ms Darbus

EAST HIGH

Attention all students! Please collect your student ID cards from the office by the end of the week.

Principal Matsui

Would the cheerleader who left her pom-poms in the canteen please collect them immediately!

Coach Bolton

Calling all artists! Volunteers needed to paint the set of the winter musical. If you're interested, please ask Ryan for details.

Sharpay

High school ID

Grab a pen and fill in the student ID cards!

Fill In Your Own Student ID!

HIGH SCHOOL ID

Name: Gabriella Montez

Clubs and activities:

_____

_____

_____

HIGH SCHOOL ID

Name: Troy Bolton

Clubs and activities:

_____

_____

_____

HIGH SCHOOL ID

Name: Sharpay Evans

Clubs and activities:

_____

_____

_____

HIGH SCHOOL ID

Name: Ryan Evans

Clubs and activities:

_____

_____

_____

_____

HIGH SCHOOL ID

Name: Taylor McKessie

Clubs and activities:

_____

_____

_____

_____

HIGH SCHOOL ID

Name: Chad Danforth

Clubs and activities:

_____

_____

_____

_____

Name: _____

Clubs and activities:

_____

_____

_____

_____

STICK A PHOTO OF YOURSELF HERE

Fill in the ID cards!

11

Which East High Wildcat would you sing on stage with? Take this quiz to find out!

1 You're in the school canteen and someone spills their lunch all over you. What do you say?

a. "Hey, don't worry about it. I'll wash it off in the bathroom."

b. "Great idea! Let's have a food fight!"

c. "Like, do you even know how much this top cost?"

2 You're doing a class project and you get partnered-up with the new girl. What happens next?

a. You invite her to hang out with you at lunch.

b. You ask her to the gym to watch your next match.

c. You tell her that she can be your new make-up artist.

3 You've have to sing in front of the class, but you've got major stage fright! What do you do?

a. Close your eyes and feel the music.

b. Have a chat to your friends backstage.

c. Do some dramatic voice exercises.

4 You're out shopping for accessories. What catches your eye?

a. A gorgeously girlie bracelet.

b. Not much, you'd rather buy a cool pair of trainers!

c. Anything sparkly. You're all about the bling!

musical match?

Gabriella Montez

Wow! You and Gabriella are practically twins! You're both as super-sweet as each other and you have exactly the same approach to life! You'd make great stage partners, cos you're both caring, cute and talented!

MOSTLY As

Troy Bolton

You're an easy-going type, who loves the sporty life - you and Troy would make a great team! With your energy and Troy's awesome dance moves, you'd be sure to dazzle the crowd with a duet or two! Go team!

MOSTLY Bs

Sharpay Evans

You and Sharpay are drama royalty! With you two up on stage, the spotlights would have to work twice as hard! You're both determined to make it to the top and you're willing to work hard to get there! Go for it!

MOSTLY Cs

13

All about Gabriella

Sharpen up your brainpower with this wordsearch all about Gabriella!
Words can run forwards, backwards and diagonally!

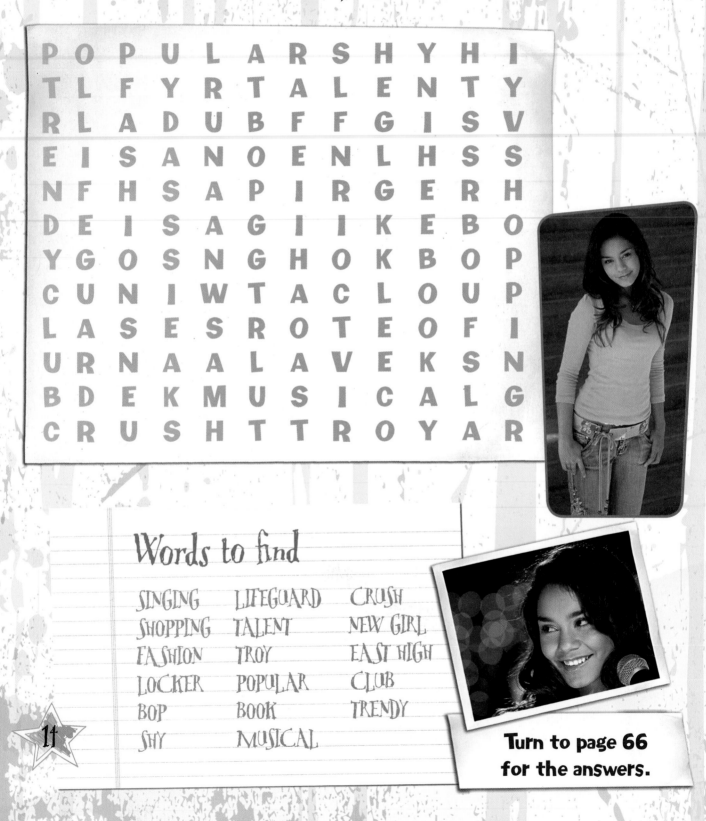

```
P O P U L A R S H Y H I
T L F Y R T A L E N T Y
R L A D U B F F G I S V
E I S A N O E N L H S S
N F H S A P I R G E R H
D E I S A G I I K E B O
Y G O S N G H O K B O P
C U N I W T A C L O U P
L A S E S R O T E O F I
U R N A A L A V E K S N
B D E K M U S I C A L G
C R U S H T T R O Y A R
```

Words to find

SINGING   LIFEGUARD   CRUSH
SHOPPING   TALENT   NEW GIRL
FASHION   TROY   EAST HIGH
LOCKER   POPULAR   CLUB
BOP   BOOK   TRENDY
SHY   MUSICAL

11

Turn to page 66 for the answers.

MY WINTER JOURNAL
By Gabriella Montez

I thought I knew exactly who I was before the winter vacation. I was the smart one, the math girl, the girl least likely to sing. But then I met Troy Bolton at the New Year's party at the Sky Mountain Ski Resort and things began to change.

Suddenly, I was singing in front of the crowd with Troy by my side!

I felt shy at first...

...but then I let go and lost myself in the music!

Troy and I swapped numbers but I couldn't help wondering if I would ever see him again. Then I moved to Albuquerque and started at East High. I couldn't believe it when I found out he was in my class!

Being the new girl at East High didn't seem so bad with Troy around.

Our first meeting didn't go smoothly and somehow we both wound up in detention, along with Troy's friend, Chad and a girl called Taylor.

Taylor's the captain of the Scholastic Decathlon team.

Chad's a basketball player, too.

I found out that Troy is the captain of the Wildcats!

After class, Troy and I had the chance to talk. It was just so great to see him again! While we were talking, we noticed a sign-up sheet for the winter musical.

This is Sharpay Evans . . .

. . . and this is her twin brother, Ryan.

Suddenly, a blonde girl marched up to us. It was Sharpay Evans, the president of the drama club! She thought I wanted to sign up for the musical!

Later on, somebody put a page from my old school's website in Taylor's locker. When she found out I was talented at maths she asked me to join the Scholastic Decathlon team!

I DON'T WANT TO BE THE FREAKY GENIUS GIRL AGAIN!

When audition day for the winter musical came around, Troy was worried about what his team mates would think and I was totally nervous, but somehow we managed to get a callback!

After that, things started getting a little crazy! Sharpay and Ryan were angry that Troy and I were going in for the second auditions. Chad and the rest of the Wildcats wanted Troy to concentrate on basketball. And Taylor still wanted me to join the Scholastic Decathlon team! It was all so confusing!

Everything seemed complicated, but we just knew that we had to keep singing!

Eventually, Chad and Taylor realised that it was okay for us to try something new. With their support, we made it to the callback auditions and won the lead roles in the winter musical!

I helped Taylor and the Scholastic Decathlon team win the championships.

As well as winning the lead role, Troy helped his team win their basketball game!

Beady bracelet

Make a beautiful bracelet to match Gabriella's dress!

WHAT YOU NEED:

★ Safety pins
★ Small red
and pink beads
★ Yellow round beads
★ 2 x 20cm
elastic

1

Thread some small
beads on to an open
safety pin. Do it up when
you've finished. Now
thread beads on to the
rest of the safety pins.
Choose any pattern
you like!

2

Thread a safety pin on to the elastic, then thread on a round bead and another safety pin. Keep going until all the safety pins are attached, then knot the ends of elastic.

3

Take the other piece of elastic and thread it through the bottom of the safety pin. Then thread a round bead between each safety pin, just like before! Tie the ends together.

Ask an adult to help!

Confidence tips

Don't let an attack of the jitters get in the way of your fun! Get sorted with these handy confidence-boosting tips!

SCHOOL SPEECH

The dilemma: You've got to give a speech at school and your stomach is totally in knots!

Get confident: Prepare what you're going to say before the day and you'll feel heaps better! Try reading out your speech in front of your family to get some practise, too! When speech day arrives, you'll be totally ready to face the crowds!

YOU'RE NEW!

The dilemma: You're the new kid in the class and you don't know anyone! Aaargh!

Get confident: Smile at your new classmates, and try to get chatting with them as soon as you can. Ask to borrow a pen or tell the girl sitting next to you that you like her bag. People love being able to help out and a compliment always breaks the ice!

STAGE FRIGHT!

The dilemma: It's the night of the school play and your legs have turned to jelly!

Get confident: Stage fright happens to everyone, even top Hollywood actors, so don't worry if you're feeling nervous. Take some deep breaths to calm yourself down, run through some Sharpay-style voice exercises, then strut your stuff like the star you are!

TOP TIP!

Hold your head up when you walk, you'll feel loads more confident!

TOP TIP!

Wear something you feel good in for a quick confidence boost!

TOP TIP!

Don't forget to smile, even if you're feeling shy!

PARTY JITTERS!

The dilemma: You've been invited to a party and you don't know the other guests! Eeek!
Get confident: Offer to take around some snacks, then you've got a reason to get chatting with everyone! Chances are, everyone else will be feeling nervous as well! Introduce yourself and find out how everyone knows your friend. You'll be dancing together in no time!

23

Get on stage

Will you make it to the stage for auditions? Race round the board to find out who'll bag the leading role - it could be YOU!

START

You bagged a straight A report card. Neat! Hop forward one.

Uh-oh, Principal Matsui busts you ditching class. Miss a turn!

You Will need:
★ A dice.
★ A counter for each player

How To play:
★ Place your counters at the start.
★ Roll the dice to start the game – the highest number goes first.
★ Race your way around the board to see who makes the auditions on time!

Sharpay's locker bursts open right in your path! Go back one.

Oops, the dog ate your homework (again!) Miss a turn.

Yikes, you've spilt your can of pop all over your song sheets! **Go back one.**

CONGRATULATIONS
You're a star. You've bagged the leaing role!
TIME TO WRITE YOUR NAME IN LIGHTS
....

You've got a serious case of last minute jitters! **Miss a go.**

FINISH

Nip to the Music Room for a last minute warmup. **Roll again.**

Cripes, your rival locks you in the Janitor's cupboard. **Miss a go!**

Too much cheering at the Wildcats game has given you a sore throat! **Go back two.**

Phew, you remembered to wear your lucky charm! **Go forward one.**

25

School's out

How quickly can you solve the search? Set your timer and check your score when you've found all the words! Will you be on dishwasher duty tonight?

```
G F K S T A R D A Z Z L E X
L F A B U L O U S R W S O O
M A W R E D H A W K S U T M
L I V A K P H E I G A N A R
N I C A I G L O M B W S L F
E G F R S T D H M H I H E U
P V O E O P E I I N L I N L
I G M L G P R R N S D N T T
C S S A F U H I G G C E S O
N Z D P F C A O N R A U H N
I A V L J E A R N G T S O Z
C S U M M E R R D E S I W V
F B T B A S K E T B A L L H
V A C A T I O N L W Y F C R
```

YOUR SCORE

More than 20 Minutes = You're fired!

15 - 20 minutes = You're on dishwasher duty!

10 - 15 minutes = Good job, take the night off!

5 - 10 minutes = You've got a promotion!

0 - 5 minutes = Wow! You're unbelievable!

Words to find

LAVA SPRINGS
BASKETBALL
SWIMMING
TALENT SHOW
MICROPHONE
VACATION

GOLF CART
MR FULTON
WILDCATS
SUMMER
LIFEGUARD
WAITER

STAR DAZZLE
FABULOUS
PICNIC
RED HAWKS
SUNSHINE

Turn to page 66 for the answers.

26

Dressing room

These pics may look exactly the same, but there are five differences in picture 2. Can you spot them all?

1

★SHARPAY★

2

★ RYAN ★

Turn to page 66 for the answers!

27

The East High gang are a talented bunch! Sneek a peek at their yearbook profiles . . .

THE STARS

Name: Troy Bolton

Likes: Basketball, cheeseburgers and Gabriella!

Star talent: He's a whizz on a basketball court!

Fave colour: Red.

Fave place: The rooftop garden at school.

Fave animal: Wolf.

Fave way to chill out: Basketball, basketball and more basketball! Troy just LOVES shooting hoops in the backyard!

Name: Gabriella Montez

Likes: Maths, singing, pizza and Troy!

Star talent: Just give her a microphone and she'll show you!

Fave colour: Peach.

Fave place: The rooftop garden at school.

Fave animal: Koala bear.

Fave way to chill out: Reading a good book.

talented

Name: Ryan Evans

Likes: Singing, singing and er, more singing!

Star talent: Being a total fashion icon and an amazing singer and dancer!

Fave colour: Turquoise.

Fave place: On stage!

Fave animal: Otter.

Fave way to chill out: When Ryan's not on stage he LOVES dancing around his living room!

Name: Sharpay Evans

Likes: Being the centre of attention.

Star talent: She's East High's leading lady!

Fave colour: Pink.

Fave place: Under a spotlight!

Fave animal: Lioness.

Fave way to chill out: Getting a facial at the Lava Srings Country Club.

Flip over for more talent profiles!

Name: Chad Danforth

Likes: Basketball, french fries and Taylor!

Star talent: Basketball, of course!

Fave colour: Green.

Fave place: Behind the wheel! Chad loves driving.

Fave animal: Wildcat.

Fave way to chill out: Chad just LOVES to watch stand-up comedy on TV.

Name: Taylor McKessie

Likes: Documentaries, lasagne and Chad!

Star talent: Being a total grade A student!

Fave colour: Midnight blue.

Fave place: The chemistry lab or the library.

Fave animal: Sea turtle.

Fave way to chill out: Using her brain to solve tricky sudoku puzzles.

talented cont...

Now grab a pen and fill in the profiles for you and your friend!

All about you!

Draw a picture of yourself here!

Draw a picture of your friend here!

Name: ....

Likes: ....

Star talent: ....

....

Fave colour: ....

Fave place: ....

Fave animal: ....

Fave way to chill out: ....

....

Name: ....

Likes: ....

Star talent: ....

....

Fave colour: ....

Fave place: ....

Fave animal: ....

Fave way to chill out: ....

....

31

High school hair

Wish you and your mates looked more like the East High crew? Just get together for a makeover sesh and follow these easy hair tips!

Cool Crop!

Troy's choppy crop is totally cool. To get this look, brush your hair forwards and ruffle it with your fingers, then use some strong-hold styling wax to keep it in place!

Crazy curls

Chad's funky curls are totally natural – just a touch of styling wax and he's good to go! If you don't have curly hair, use some hair stylers to create Chad's funky curls!

Sweet scarf!

Taylor's 'do is easy peasy! Tie a cute scarf around your head, then pull the long ends to the back so they're hidden by your hair. Taylor loves cute patterned scarves, like this polka dot one.

32

Pretty plaits!

Brush your hair into a centre parting and divide it into two equal sections. Loosely plait each section and secure them halfway down with a hair elastic. Curl the hair at the end of your plaits with a hair styler to complete the Gabriella look!

Hat trick!

Who needs hair tips when you've got a hat? Ryan tops off his look with a cool East High baseball cap. You too can get this super-funky look by, err, simply wearing a baseball cap. Duh!

Totally glam!

To get Sharpay's look, just brush your hair into a side parting and pull it over into a side ponytail. Use a funky hair elastic to secure it in place, then drape your pony over your shoulder and make like a drama diva! Cool!

GABRIELLA

Casual

Gabriella's style is totally sweet and girly! When she's feeling casual, she goes for a pretty top with jeans and she loves getting sporty in shorts and hoodies. She's an easy-going girl and her pretty clothes say loads about her personality! Her cute girl-next-door style is certainly a big hit with Troy!

This fitted hoodie looks fab on Gabriella.

These are officially the cutest shorts in town!

Knee-high socks are sweet 'n' sporty!

style files

Smart

When it's time to dress up, Gabriella goes for gorgeously girly dresses! She picks cute details, like ribbon trims and fabric flowers. She loves pretty prints with a surfer-girl feel just as much as flowers and frills! When it comes to shoes, Gabriella goes for trainers, ballet pumps or wedges. Sky-high heels are totally not her thing!

How gorgeous is this flowery belt?

These white wedges are pure perfection!

Gabriella looks like an angel in this girly dress.

35

EAST HIGH Presents

TROY

This retro top is totally Troy!

Casual

When it comes to fashion, Troy likes to keep it cool and casual. When he's training for a big game, he goes for something sporty, like his East High tracksuit and Wildcats vest. And when he's off the court, he chills out in jeans, cool cut-offs or combat shorts

Troy's essential accessory!

Combat shorts are great for sunny days!

style files

Smart

Troy looks great in stylish stripes.

Troy's a pretty casual guy, but that doesn't mean he can't do smart! Tailored jackets look great on his athletic frame and he loves teaming them with a cool pair of jeans and a funky shirt. When there's a special occasion, Troy always manages to put his own spin on smart dressing!

The suit jacket says, 'I'm smart!'

But the jeans say, 'I'm cool!'

37

EAST HIGH Presents

Sharpay RYAN

Sharpay

Sharpay's head-turning, attention-grabbing, spot-light-stealing style is famous at East High! She has about a million different outfits and she wouldn't dream of being seen without her accessories! She believes that it's the details that count, and if you look closely at her outfits, you'll usually notice a burst of sequins or studs.

This gorgeous jacket screams, "I mean business!"

These cute bracelets give Sharpay's outfit some extra sparkle!

How fabulous are these shoes?

36

style files

Ryan's funky hat totally co-ordinates with his shirt.

Ryan

Forget basketball shirts and casual hoodies! Ryan likes his styles sharp and smart! Hot designer jeans, super smart chinos and crisp collared shirts are what this boy's all about! Ryan loves bold designs and he often goes for funky patterns and bright colours. And have you ever seen him without his trademark hat? Didn't think so!

Ryan's footwear works the smart-casual look to the max!

Oh-la-la! Check out the sophisticated trousers!

EAST HIGH presents

TAYLOR CHAD

Taylor

Taylor's style is as smart as she is! She looks great in Otted tops and trousers and she loves wearing smart and funky jackets. When she's glamming it up, she goes for beautiful dresses in jewel colours. And when it comes to accessories she chooses super stylish bangles and hoop earrings.

Taylor's jacket is super stylish.

Great colour combination!

These cute crops are smart and chic!

style files

Looking bright in colourful stripes!

Check out the funky trainers!

Chad loves his jeans!

Chad

Chad's laid-back look totally reflects his personality. He always looks chilled-out and funky whatever he wears! Chad's a big fan of bright colours, so he's often dressed in fiery reds, sunny yellows and brilliant blues. When he's not wearing his Wildcat gear, he goes for slouchy jeans and funky t-shirts!

What's your club?

Whether you're a brainiac or a sports jock, there's a school club just for you! But which one will you be captaining this term?!

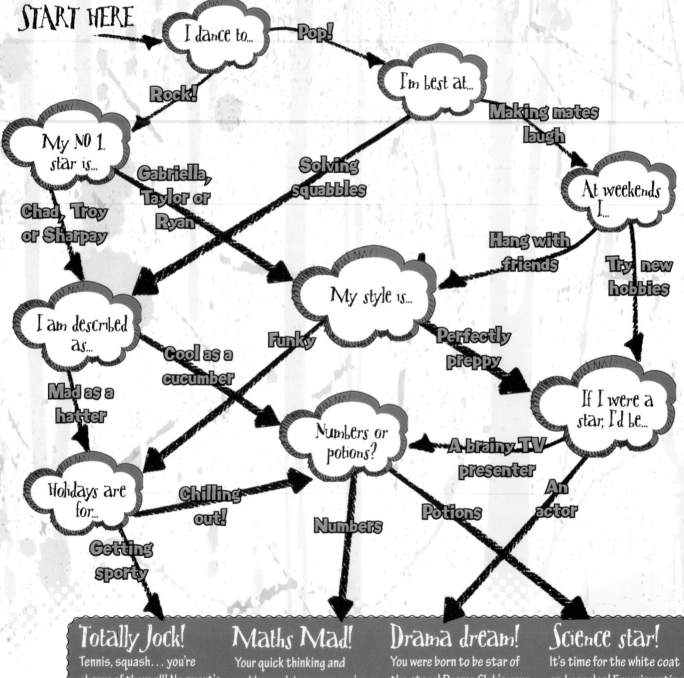

START HERE

I dance to... — Pop! → I'm best at... — Making mates laugh → At weekends I...

I dance to... — Rock! → My NO 1. star is...

I'm best at... — Solving squabbles →

My NO 1. star is... — Gabriella, Taylor or Ryan →

My NO 1. star is... — Chad, Troy or Sharpay → I am described as...

At weekends I... — Hang with friends → My style is...

At weekends I... — Try new hobbies → If I were a star, I'd be...

My style is... — Funky

My style is... — Perfectly preppy → If I were a star, I'd be...

I am described as... — Cool as a cucumber

I am described as... — Mad as a hatter → Holidays are for...

Numbers or potions?

If I were a star, I'd be... — A brainy TV presenter → Numbers or potions?

Holidays are for... — Chilling out!

Holidays are for... — Getting sporty → Totally Jock!

Numbers or potions? — Numbers → Maths Mad!

Numbers or potions? — Potions → Science star!

If I were a star, I'd be... — An actor → Drama dream!

Totally Jock!
Tennis, squash... you're champ of them all! No sport's too hard for you to master! Step aside Troy, there's a new Sports Club leader in town!

Maths Mad!
Your quick thinking and problem solving mean you're a genius in the making - you'd be the super-star brainiac of the Maths Club.

Drama dream!
You were born to be star of the stage! Drama Club's your bag because the spotlight twinkles even brighter when it shines on you.

Science star!
It's time for the white coat and goggles! Experimenting is your game and the Science Club is the perfect place to put your talents to the test!

12

Twinkle Towne

Fit all the words into the Criss Cross below and take a bow!

4 letters	5 letters	6 letters
Troy	Stage	Dances
Chad		
Ryan		

7 letters	8 letters	9 letters
Sharpay	Rehearse	Gabriella
Musical		Spotlight

A
u
d
i
t
i
o
n
s

Turn to page 66 for the answers.

Star Dazzle

13

Sleepover

Plan the perfect HSM sleepover with our quick 'n' easy tips.
Tick them off when you're done!

What time is it?

Sleepovers are all about fun, but make sure you plan in enough time for everything! Make a rough list in your head of what you want to do and when, then do it!

Work this out

That's right, you've got to work out what you're going to do! Sleepovers can be action-packed or simply snuggly PJ parties – it's totally up to you!

I don't dance

Oh yes, you do! No sleepover is complete without a bit of bopping to the top! So dig out those dance moves, hit the floor and rock out to those tunes!

You are the music in me

Whether you're grooving, giggling or gossiping, you need music! So, either grab the nearest hairbrush and provide your own karaoke-style, or stick on your fave tunes and take it in turns to play DJ!

success!

Fabulous

You've got to look your best, even at a sleepover! So before you get into full swing, prepare a pampering sesh for you and your pals, and get ready to glam it up, Sharpay style!

All for one

The more the merrier where sleepovers are concerned, but make sure everyone gets to do something they want. Stick ideas in a hat, then pull them out and try everyone's idea at random.

Sleepover Dos and Don'ts!

Don't forget to ask your parents before you invite anybody!

DO send invites out early and bagsy your friends in advance!

DON'T get upset if not everyone can make it. You'll have fun no matter what.

DO make energy-filled snacks! Try Wildcat sandwiches with cheese and tomato or Sharpay's super smoothie packed with fabulous fruit!

DON'T play your music too loud. You don't want your parents bursting in to tell you off. Mega, mega cringe!

DO have everything organised, with your games, CDs and magazines at the ready. No wasting time!

DON'T eat so much you might burst. You gotta leave room for that Wildcat dance routine!

What's your

That's right – term-time's over and you gotta get a job! Question is... which one will be keeping you out of trouble this summer?

1

You've just arrived at Lava Springs and are picking your uniforms. You choose...

a) Something cool to reflect your laid-back 'tude!

b) Uniform? Er, that was so last year, darling.

c) Anything bright and colourful that screams FUN!

d) A comfy tracksuit because you can make anything look good!

2

It's your first night at the Country Club. What would we find you doing?

a) Checking out the restaurant and cafes - you're all about the food!

b) In your room, with a cucumber face-pack and someone pampering you and your dog!

c) Dancing! Even if there's no disco - wherever you go, the party follows!

d) In the pool because it's the perfect place for cooling off after your long journey.

Mostly As - Waiting tables

Just like Chad, you're always ready to dish up the gossip and ladle out the laughs! You'd make a great addition to the kitchen crew! With your laid-back attitude and cheeky grin you'd be perfect as a Lava Springs waiter.

Mostly Bs - Lazy days!

Work? Job? Er, hel-lo? That is soo not happening! There's no waaay you'd waste your summer washing dishes! Forget that! You were made for a life of luxury - just like Sharpay! You'd spend your Lava Spring days lounging by the pool and being fabulous!

summer job?

3

It's pool party time, but oops, your mate's tripped over an inflatable donkey and fallen in. You...

a) Offer her a fruit-juice to cool her down after her refreshing swim!

b) Rush to your sun lounger to check she didn't drench it on her way in!

c) Get everyone to jump in, too and start a water aerobics sesh!

d) Jump in to rescue her!

4

Uh-oh, disaster strikes - a power-cut during dinner! You...

a) Grab some candles - not even darkness will keep you from your dinner!

b) Scream until someone comes to rescue you!

c) Initiate Plan B - a game of murder mystery!

d) Go for a moonlight swim.

Mostly Cs - Party planner

It's all party, party, party! Without you and your clipboard, the Lava Springs entertainment would just not happen! Like Taylor, you're smart, sassy and super-organised, which means you're perfect for heading up the Party Planning team.

Mostly Ds - Lovely lifeguard

When a pal's in peril, you dive right in, which is why you'd be a great lifeguard, just like Gabriella. With the safety of the Country Club residents in your capable hands... everyone's in for a splashing time.

47

Go Wildcats!

It's time to talk team tactics... words run forwards, backwards and diagonally. There are 15 to spot. Do the Wildcats proud and go find 'em!

When you've found all the words in the box, see if you can find a mystery word that isn't listed!

B A L L G A M E T H
P L A Y E T O S R I
G I N A R L R T E A
C M R U L E S D M H
O B O U N C E S E O
A C B I A R T R E O
C H A N T R O T S P
H R L R O C I O T W
T A O H S H O O T S
A Y S E W O P A R D

Words to find

TRAINERS   BOUNCE
RULES   HOOP
BALL GAME   COACH
SHOOT   SCORE
RED   WHITE
SHORTS   PLAY
COURT   CHANT

Turn to page 67 for the answers.

My Summer Journal

By Gabriella Montez

Even before the holidays began, I knew this vacation was going to be special. It was the first time in my life I was staying in the same place all summer. I just knew something cool was going to happen...

When we were all offered summer jobs by Mr Fulton, the manager of Lava Springs, it felt like our dreams had come true! It was a great chance for us to save up for college and we'd get to hang out together, too!

We wanted to hang out all summer long!

I knew working with Troy was gonna be fun!

It turned out that Lava Springs country club was owned by Sharpay and Ryan's family!

TROY

Kelsi wrote a song for me and Troy to sing at the club's annual talent show. It was great to be singing together again! I could tell Troy was happy, too!

When we practised together, it felt so special.

Everybody was thinking about the talent show, especially Sharpay.

Then suddenly, everything began to change. Troy was given a promotion and extra privileges, but the rest of us had to work harder than ever.

Troy and I stopped spending so much time together. Everything was so confusing. Part of me was pleased Troy was doing so well with his job and part of me was sad that things had changed between us.

We'd had so much fun together, but everything was different now. I knew I had to make a decision. It was time to go my own way.

Things were going well for Troy, but our relationship was suffering...

WILDCATS

Luckily, our friends were there for both of us. They got us back on stage together, and we sung our duet at the Star Dazzle talent contest.

Our worries melted away as we lost ourselves in the song. It felt like we were the old Gabriella and Troy again. Everybody was happy, even Sharpay!

The next day, there was a pool party for all the staff! As I swam with Troy and all our friends and it felt like all my summer wishes had come true!

FRIENDS FOREVER!

53

Tips for the top!

Get ready to hit the big time with Sharpay and Ryan's showbiz guide to life!

Make it happen!

Remember that a lot of work goes on backstage. Be prepared to learn new things if you want to be fabulous!

Reach for the stars!

"You can't star in your school play if you don't put your name down to audition! Tell people that you want to join in, so you get YOUR chance to shine! The same goes for anything else you want to try out, sports, arty stuff - whatever! Tell your teachers that you want to take part and make it happen!"

Show the world how fabulous you are by joining a school club. Pick an activity you enjoy and just go for it!

"Don't hide backstage with all the dusty props - nobody will notice you if you hang-out in the shadows! Hold your head up high and stand in the spotlight! If you want to reach the top, you've got to act like you belong there! Believe in yourself and other people will believe in you, too. Let your light shine!"

"If you like singing and dancing, you need to practise every day before you can put on the perfect performance! Even mega talented people need to practise their skills, you know! Aim high, work hard and reach for the stars! Remember, there are no lazy people at the top - only gorgeous hard working ones like moi!"

Being fabulous is about being the best you can be. Practise your talents, whatever they are and be proud to be yourself.

"Let's face it, working with other people can be hard . . . especially when they won't do what you want. But remember that there's always something new to learn, even if you are totally perfect like moi! And if you let other people have their own way, they'll be more likely to let you have your own way later!"

55

Summer secrets

Gabriella has slipped a postcard into Troy's backpack on her way to the pool. Can you work out what it says?

G=★ A=★ B=★ R=★ I=★ E=★ L=★ L=★ A=★

T=★ R=★ O=★ Y=★

Hi Troy,
★u★ss wh★★? ★h★★★'s
★★n★ ★★★ ★★ ★ p★★★
p★★★★ ★★m★★★★w!
w★'★★ ★★★★★★ h★n★
★u★ ★★★★ ★h★★ ★★★
d★★! h★w c★★★ ★s ★h★★?

From Gabriella

WISH YOU WERE HERE ...

Turn to page **67**
for the answers.

What team?

How many times does the word 'Wildcats' appear in the grid below?

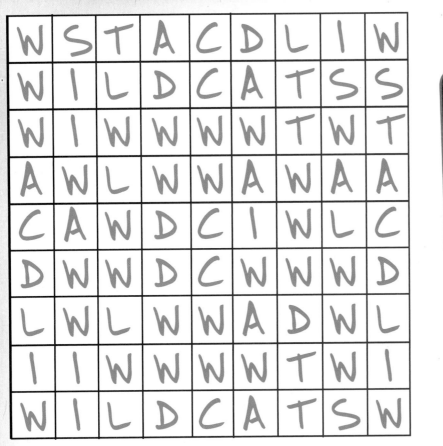

W	S	T	A	C	D	L	I	W
W	I	L	D	C	A	T	S	S
W	I	W	W	W	W	T	W	T
A	W	L	W	W	A	W	A	A
C	A	W	D	C	I	W	L	C
D	W	W	D	C	W	W	W	D
L	W	L	W	W	A	D	W	L
I	I	W	W	W	W	T	W	I
W	I	L	D	C	A	T	S	W

Turn to page 67 for the answers.

Fabulous forfeits

School's out and you've bagged yourself a luxury trip to Lava Springs! All you have to do is complete the forfeits and get from East High to the country club before your friends!

You will need:
★ A counter for each player and a dice.

What to do
★ Place your counters at the start and take it in turns to roll the dice and move around the board.
★ If you land on a forfeit and complete it, you get to move forward one extra square!

START
Do an impression of Ms Darbus. And move forward one!

Pick your fave character and act out one of their scenes, then move on one!

Sing your fave *High School Musical 2* song backwards, then go forwards one!

Make up a dance routine to 'Work This Out', then move forward one!

Grab a partner and duet to 'All For One', then move on one!

Congratulations! You're off to Lava Springs!

Do as many character impressions as you can in one minute. If the players guess more than three, jump to the finish!

Do an impression of Sharpay! If you make everyone laugh, go forward one.

The Future is a Big Place

Challenge one mate to a dance off! The last one dancing moves forward one square - but it might not be you!

Sing 'You Are the Music in Me' in the style of your fave character, then hop forward one.

Star Dazzle

Do you have what it takes to solve
this star-studded sudoku?

What to do . . .

Each member of the gang should appear once in every row and
column of the grid. Work out who's missing and write their
initials in the blank spaces!

Turn to page **67**
for the answers.

60

You've been framed

Somebody's pinched a piece from Sharpay's photo, so it's up to you to work out which piece fits. Get the picture?

Turn to page 68 for the answers.

61

ENROL AT

WANT TO BE A STUDENT AT EAST HIGH?

JUST FILL IN THIS FORM AND GET READY FOR CLASS!

STICK A
PHOTO
OF YOURSELF
HERE

Name ....

Date of birth ....

Friendship is important at East High! Please write the names of your three best friends here. We will do our best to put you all in the same class.

1 ....

2 ....

3 ....

Which of the following subjects would you like to study this year?
Please note: ALL students MUST study Maths and English.

Maths ☐   English ☐   Art ☐   French ☐

Science ☐   Geography ☐   PSHE ☐   Music ☐

PE ☐   Design ☐   RE ☐

Best school subject ....

Worst school subject ....

Which school clubs would you be interested in joining?
Tick as many boxes as you like!

Drama club ☐	Fashion club ☐	Chemistry club ☐
Book club ☐	Hip-hop club ☐	Music society ☐
Basketball club ☐	Cookery class ☐	Gymnastics club ☐
Ballet club ☐	School band ☐	Skate club ☐

Thank you for filling in The East High enrolment form.
You are now officially a student of the school.

Your student buddy is Gabriella Montez.
She will show you around East High and
make you feel welcome.

"CLASSES START EARLY...

DON'T BE LATE."

High school

How much do you really know about High School Musical and High School Muscial 2? Take this test and find out!

Q1. What song did Gabriella and Troy sing when they first met?

_____

Q2. Who owns Lava Springs Country Club?

_____

Q3. Circle the hat that belongs to Kelsi!

a) 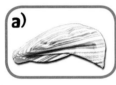   **b)**    **c)**

Q4. What's the name of East High's principal?

a)   Principal Matsui   ◯

b)   Principal Matt   ◯

c)   Principal Sue   ◯

Q5. Who likes to cook crème brûlée?

Zeke ◯   Chad ◯   Troy ◯

musical quiz

Q6. Which high school girl sings Humuhumunukunukuapua'A?

 ◯    ◯

Q7. What job does Gabriella do at Lava Springs Country Club?

a) Chambermaid ◯

b) Lifeguard ◯

Q8. Who is Taylor McKessie's best girlfriend?

Gabriella   Sharpay

Q9. What's the name of the winter musical?

a) Twinkle Toes ◯

b) Twinkle Towne ◯

Q10. What letter is on the necklace Troy gave to Gabriella?

a) S for summer ◯

b) T for Troy ◯

Turn to page 68 for the answers.

 65

PUZZLE ANSWERS

P14 All about Gabriella

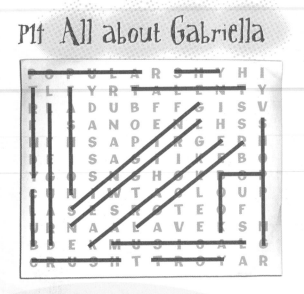

P27 Dressing room

★RYAN

P26 School's out

P43 Twinkle Towne

CHAD
AUDITIONS
SHARPAY / RYAN
GABRIELLA
DANCES
TROY
REHEARSE
SPOTLIGHT
MUSICAL
STAGE

Star Dazzle

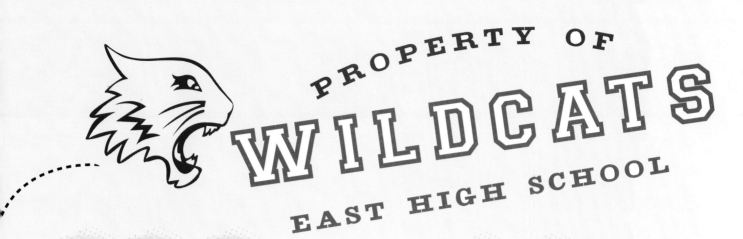

PROPERTY OF WILDCATS
EAST HIGH SCHOOL

P48 Go Wildcats!

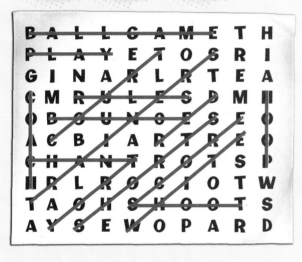

BALLGAMETH
PLAYETOSRI
GINARLRTEA
CMRULESDMI
OBOUNCESEO
ACBIARTREE
CHANTROTSP
HRLROGIOTW
TAOHSHOOTS
AYSEWOPARD

P57 What team?

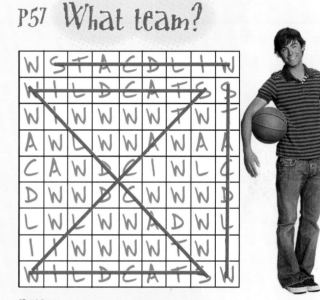

WSTACDLIW
WILDCATSS
WWWWWTWT
AWDWWAWAA
CAWDCIWLC
DWWDCWWWD
LWLWWADWL
IIWWWWTW
WILDCATSW

Wildcats appears six times.

P56 Summer secrets

Hi Troy,
Guess what? There's
going to be a pool
party tomorrow!
We'll get to hang out
together all day! How
cool is that?

From Gabriella

P60 Star Dazzle

67

PUZZLE ANSWERS CONT...

p61 You've been framed

p64-65 High school musical quiz

1) Start of something new.
2) Sharpay and Ryan's parents
3) a.
4) Principal Matsui.
5) Zeke

6) Sharpay.
7) Lifeguard.
8) Gabriella.
9) Twinkle Towne.
10) T for Troy.